THE KIDS' BOOK OF 14 AWESOME ACTIVITIES

By
Tony Tallarico

kidsbooks
Incorporated

Hours of challenging fun and games are
in store for you in

THE KIDS' BOOK
OF AWESOME ACTIVITIES.

Each book is chock full of secret codes, mazes,
hidden picture puzzles, word finds, riddles,
crosswords, things to draw, and many other
zany activities. There's never a dull moment,
so get ready to have a blast as you test your
skills trying to solve these awesome puzzles.

What are you waiting for? Sharpen your
pencil and let's go!

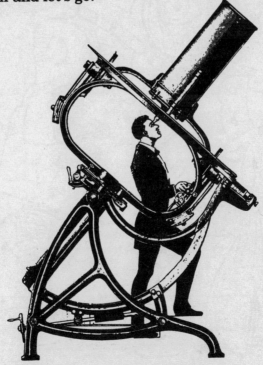

Answers begin on page 152.

A KEEN EYE

CAN YOU HELP THIS DETECTIVE
FIND THE FOLLOWING LETTERS
AND NUMBERS IN THIS SCENE?
A · B · C · D · E · F
1 · 2 · 3 · 4 · 5 · 6

A-MAZE-ING CAT

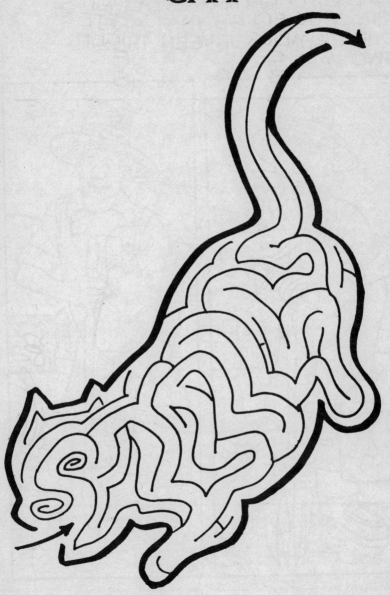

WHAT'S DIFFERENT?

CIRCLE **6** THINGS THAT ARE DIFFERENT BETWEEN THESE TWO FARMERS.

DOWN AND ACROSS

ANSWER THESE CLUES AND WRITE
THEM IN THEIR CORRECT SPACES.
THE COMPLETED ANSWERS WILL
READ THE SAME DOWN AND
ACROSS.

1- OPPOSITE OF STAND
2- FROZEN WATER
3- SEVEN PLUS THREE EQUAL __

	1.	2.	3.
1.			
2.			
3.			

CLUES...CLUES

WRITE THE ANSWER TO EACH CLUE. THEN LIST THE CIRCLED LETTERS, IN THE ORDER THAT THEY APPEAR, TO FORM THE MYSTERY WORD.

NOT OPENED	◯ _ ◯ _ _
TEN CENTS OR A —	_ _ ◯ _
OPPOSITE OF PULL	◯◯ _ _
TO EXCHANGE OR SWAP	◯ _ _ _ ◯
A SPRING MONTH	_ _ ◯ _ _

MYSTERY WORD:

_ _ _ _ _ _ _

8

MAKE-A-WORD

Create your own list of words using the letters from:
EASTER EGG

"LET'S READ!"

FIND AND CIRCLE THESE WORDS HAVING TO DO WITH YOUR PUBLIC LIBRARY.

B—Biography, Books, Borrow; **C**—Card, Catalogue, Classic, Comedy, Counter; **D**—Date, Dictionary, Drama; **E**—Edition, Encyclopedia; **F**—Fiction, Film, Fun; **H**—Help; **L**—Librarian, List, Locate; **M**—Magazine ; **N**—Notes, Novel, Number; **P**—Part, Pamphlet, Plays, Poetry, Prints; **R**—Rack, Read, Research, Return, Room; **S**—Seat, Shelf, Story; **T**—Table, Tome

```
B E U G O L A T A C S Y A L P
D I N O I T I D E L K C A R S
I L O C A T E S D A E R C K F
C I T G N O V E L S R O O M I
T B E A R P T L I S T O M L C
I R L D R A C N E I B D E I T
O A H T D R P P S C O R D F I
N R P A F L E H S S R A Y H O
A I M E W O R K Y T R M R C N
R A A S S E M O T O O A E R P
Y N P E T A B L E R W T T A R
F E T N U M B E R Y W R U E I
U O U M A G A Z I N E A R S N
N O P L E H Y R T E O P N E T
C E N C Y C L O P E D I A R S
```

HOMONYMS

HOMONYMS ARE WORDS THAT SOUND THE SAME BUT ARE SPELLED DIFFERENTLY AND HAVE DIFFERENT MEANINGS. CHOOSE THE CORRECT WORD FOR EACH SENTENCE.

IS A HAMBURGER — **MEET** OR **MEAT** ?

IS APPLE PIE — **SWEET** OR **SUITE** ?

IS THE OPPOSITE OF OLD — **KNEW** OR **NEW** ?

DOES A BOAT SET — **SAIL** OR **SALE** ?

DOES AN AUTHOR — **RIGHT** OR **WRITE** ?

DOES A QUEEN SIT ON A — **THROWN** OR **THRONE** ?

LINK-UP PUZZLE

Place these words in the correct spaces.
Then write the circled letters in numerical order to
form the mystery words.

4 LETTERS
TOLL

5 LETTERS
STORM

6 LETTERS
AUTUMN

7 LETTERS
COSTUME
FRIENDS

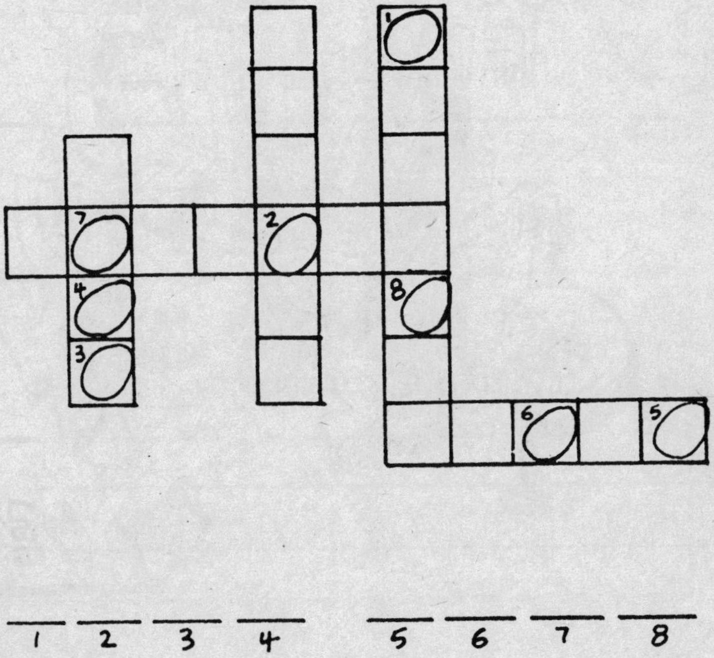

_ _ _ _   _ _ _ _
1 2 3 4   5 6 7 8

ALPHABET MAZE
FOLLOW THE PATH THROUGH THE
ALPHABET FROM **A** TO **Z**.

UNSCRAMBLE

UNSCRAMBLE THE NAMES OF THESE TWO U.S. PRESIDENTS.

2ND PRESIDENT

JOHN

AAMDS

_____

4TH PRESIDENT

JAMES

DIMANSO

_____

FIND AND CIRCLE

FIND AND CIRCLE **10** THINGS THAT ARE
DIFFERENT BETWEEN THESE TWO SCENES.

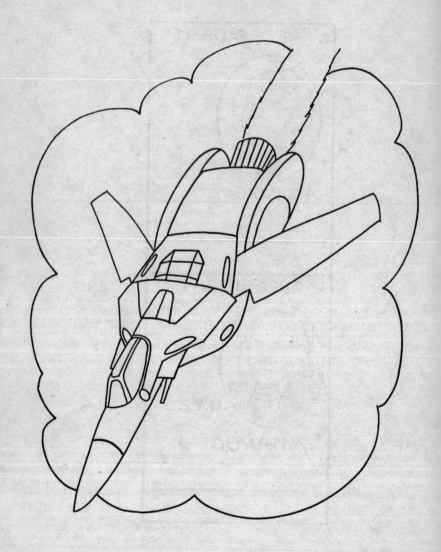

UNSCRAMBLE

LNDA

_ _ O _

LGAD

O _ _ _

RAIPL

_ O O O _

SUHOE

O _ _ _ _ O

SYON

O _ _ _

OLDSI

O O _ _ _

LIST AND UNSCRAMBLE THE CIRCLED LETTERS.

THIS HAPPENS EVERYTIME YOU STEP INTO THE SHOWER...

SCRAMBLED LETTERS:

_ _ _ _ _ _ _ _ _ _

UNSCRAMBLED ANSWER:

THE _ _ _ _ _
_ _ _ _ _ !!

SECRET JOKE

USE THE CHART TO DECODE THE ANSWER TO THIS JOKE.

WHAT'S A GOOD THING THAT CATS CAN'T DO ?

	1	2	3	4	5
A	D	E	I	T	L
B	I	Q	W	R	Z
C	B	L	A	P	E
D	K	J	S	I	H

<u>B3</u>   <u>D5</u>   <u>B1</u>   <u>D3</u>   <u>A4</u>   <u>C2</u>   <u>A2</u>

<u>A5</u>   <u>D4</u>   <u>D1</u>   <u>C5</u>

<u>C3</u>

<u>C1</u>   <u>A3</u>   <u>B4</u>   <u>A1</u> !

MYSTERY PIX

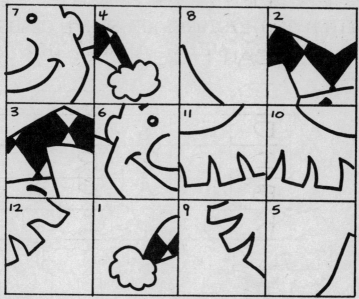

DRAW WHAT YOU SEE FROM THE NUMBERED BOXES
ABOVE INTO THE SAME NUMBERED BOXES BELOW.

1	2	3	4
5	6	7	8
9	10	11	12

TWINS

WHICH TWO PICTURES OF SANTA CLAUS ARE EXACTLY ALIKE? CIRCLE THEM.

GULP!!

HOW MANY PEANUTS CAN A
GIANT APE EAT IN FIVE SECONDS?
COUNT CAREFULLY AS MANY OF
THEM OVERLAP.

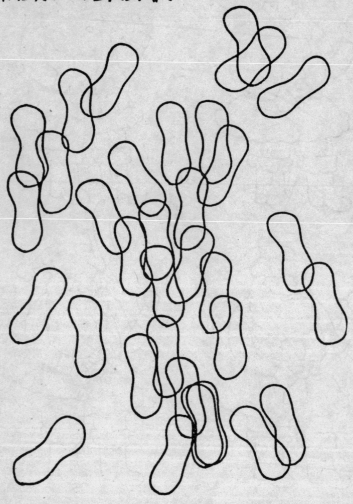

_____
TOTAL

A FLYING CUP
AND SAUCER!

UNSCRAMBLE

UNSCRAMBLE EACH
WORD AND WRITE IT
IN ITS CORRECT
NUMBER PLACE TO FORM
A SENTENCE.

ARDGEN	11-	GARDEN
UNF	2-	
OMM	6-	
HEPL	4-	
TEH	10-	
IST'	1-	
DDA	8-	
OT	3-	
YROU	5-	
NI	9-	
ADN	7-	

1- _____ ' 2- _____ 3- _____

4- _____ 5- _____

6- _____ 7- _____ 8- _____

9- _____ 10- _____

11- G A R D E N .

MAZE

HELP THIS SNOWMAN REACH WINTERLAND BEFORE HE MELTS!

WINTER LAND

FIND AND LAUGH

ON THE LAST DAY OF SCHOOL.

FIND - ☐☐ APPLES(2) • ☐ BALLOON
☐ CRAYON • ☐ DOG • ☐ HAMMER
☐☐ PENCILS(2) • ☐ STAR • ☐ UMBRELLA

ARE YOU GOING ON A VACATION?

YES, I HEARD MY DAD SAY THAT HIS BOSS WAS GIVING HIM A GUILT TRIP!

I'VE GOT TWO MONTHS TO RECOVER FROM TEACHING THIS SCHOOL YEAR.

YOU'RE LUCKY... I'M TEACHING SUMMER SCHOOL.

DISCOVER IT

AMERICA   MONDAY
CHRISTOPHER   OCTOBER
DISCOVER   SEARCH
EXPLORE   SEEK
FIND   SHIPS
HONOR   SPAIN
ITALIAN   TRAVEL
JOURNEY   VOYAGE
LEARN

Find these words about **COLUMBUS DAY**.
They go up, down, forward, backward, and
diagonally.

```
T   R   V   O   Y   A   G   E   C
D   O   N   S   E   J   H   L   H
R   N   K   E   N   G   N   E   R
Y   O   E   A   R   H   R   V   I
A   H   E   R   U   C   A   A   S
D   I   S   C   O   V   E   R   T
N   T   C   H   J   L   L   T   O
O   A   C   H   I   R   P   Z   P
M   L   N   I   A   P   S   X   H
F   I   N   D   A   M   S   R   E
C   A   M   E   R   I   C   A   R
C   N   R   E   B   O   T   C   O
```

A PUZZLING PUZZLE

THE WORD *PUZZLE* APPEARS
7 TIMES IN THE GRID BELOW.
CAN YOU FIND AND CIRCLE THEM?

```
Z P U Z Z L E
P Z L Z P L L
P P U P L L Z
E Z U U Z E Z
L Z Z Z L P U
Z E L Z Z U P
Z Z Z L U L P
U U U E P P E
P E L L Z U P
```

MAZE

HELP HER REACH HOME
BEFORE THE ICE CREAM
SHE IS CARRYING
MELTS.

FIND AND CIRCLE...

THE FOLLOWING HIDDEN LETTERS
ON THIS CREATURE FROM SPACE,
A · B · C · D · E · F · G · H

PETE and RE-PETE

16 I	5 I	10 E	11 T	15 I
21 S	2 W	3 N	22 R	6 I
8 E	9 T	14 U	1 R	13 A
7 I	24 D	17 N	18 G	12 W
20 T	23 I	4 R	27 N	25 G

_ _ _ _ _ '

_ _ _ _ _ _ _ _ !

DIFFERENT

THREE OF THESE EGGS ARE EXACTLY
THE SAME. WHICH ONE IS DIFFERENT?

HOW MANY?

HOW MANY TIMES DOES THE WORD **BIRD** APPEAR BELOW? CIRCLE AND COUNT EACH.

BIRD B

BIRD I

R B R

DBIRD D

B RBB

BIRD I I

R D R R

D D D

TOTAL

SNOWBALL MAZE

GUIDE THE SNOWBALL!

MYSTERY PIX

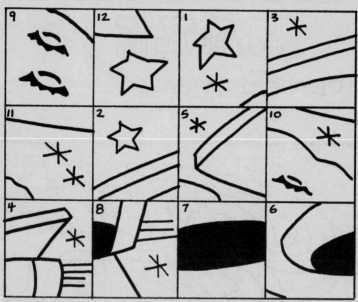

DRAW WHAT YOU SEE FROM THE NUMBERED BOXES ABOVE INTO THE SAME NUMBERED BOXES BELOW.

1	2	3	4
5	6	7	8
9	10	11	12

WHAT'S WRONG?
FIND **7** THINGS WRONG HERE.

WHAT'S WRONG

FIND AND CIRCLE 6 THINGS THAT ARE WRONG IN THIS PICTURE.

FILL IN

FILL IN THE AREAS THAT CONTAIN A DOT
TO FORM AN UNLUCKY NUMBER!

HIDDEN

GO THROUGH THIS MAZE, USING A DARK PENCIL, TO SEE WHAT'S HIDDEN HERE.

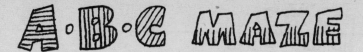

A·B·C MAZE

Reach the gift by correctly going through the alphabet maze.

SPOT-A-PIX

• SAFARI PARK •

(STAY IN YOUR CAR)

☐ APPLE
☐ BALLOON
☐ BRUSH
☐ CAMERA
☐ FIRE HYDRANT
☐ FORK
☐ KITE
☐ LOST SNEAKER
☐ SKATEBOARD
☐ SOCK
☐ SUNGLASSES
☐ TRASH CAN
☐ TV SET
☐ WREATH

47

A PUZZLING

SOLVE THIS CROSSWORD — THE PICTURE CLUES WILL HELP YOU.

ACROSS:

1- A FARM ANIMAL

4- ONE WHO FLIES A **PLANE**

6- OPPOSITE OF SOUTH

7- OPPOSITE OF RIGHT

8- DAY BEFORE TUESDAY

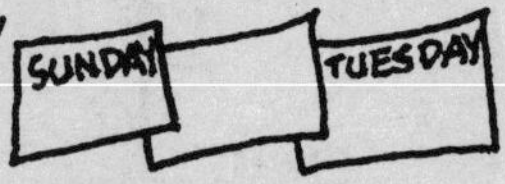

DOWN:

2- FIRST U.S. PRESIDENT

3- MOVIE SNACK

5- OPPOSITE OF STAND

CROSSWORD

DIFFERENT

OUT OF THESE 5 BASEBALL PLAYERS,
WHICH ONE IS DIFFERENT?   CIRCLE
THE DIFFERENT ONE.

JUST JOKING

USE THIS CHART TO DECODE THE SOLUTION TO THIS QUESTION —

A - 1   R - 9
C - 2   S - 10
E - 3   T - 11
F - 4   U - 12
I - 5   Y - 13
N - 6
O - 7
P - 8

HOW DO YOU MAKE SOUP GOLD?

PETE

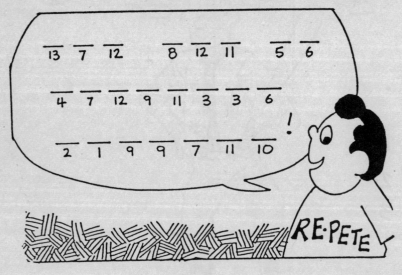

13 7 12   8 12 11   5 6

4 7 12 9 11 3 3 6

2 1 9 9 7 11 10   !

RE·PETE

TWO WAYS!

ANSWER THESE CLUES AND WRITE THEM IN THEIR CORRECT SPACES. THE COMPLETED ANSWERS WILL READ THE SAME DOWN AND ACROSS.

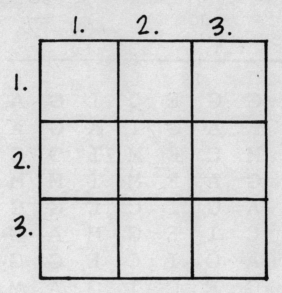

1- OPPOSITE OF WOMAN.

2- HAD SOME PIZZA.

3- NOT OLD.

FIND THEM!

HOW MANY TIMES IS THE PHRASE –
MAGIC   EGG
HIDDEN IN THIS PUZZLE? CIRCLE AND
COUNT EACH.

```
M  G  G  E  C  I  G  A  M
A  E  A  G  I  A  G  A  G
G  M  C  E  M  I  G  C  G
I  G  A  E  M  I  M  M  E
M  A  G  I  C  E  G  G  C
C  C  I  E  G  M  A  G  I
M  A  G  I  C  E  G  G  G
G  G  E  C  I  G  A  M  A
M  A  G  I  E  G  C  G  M
```

_____
TOTAL

BUTTERFLY CHASE MAZE!

FIND 10 THINGS THAT ARE DIFFERENT

BETWEEN THESE TWO PICTURES.

CROSS OUT

CROSS OUT ALL THE LETTERS THAT
APPEAR 5 TIMES ONLY. LIST THE
REMAINING LETTERS IN THE SPACES
BELOW.

O	L	E	A	T	U
S	L	U	I	O	G
U	H	T	W	A	W
W	O	U	T	H	W
E	T	U	R	A	O
A	O	E	A	W	E

_ _ _ ' _

_ _ _ _ _ _ _ _

_ _ _ _ !

58

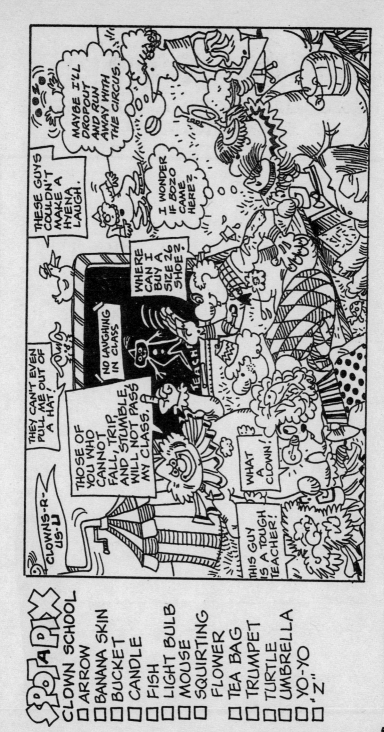

MAKE-A-WORD

Create your own list of words using the letters from:
VEGETABLE GARDEN

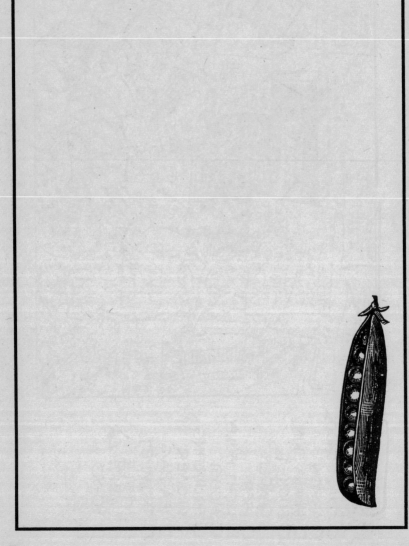

FILL IN

FILL IN THE AREAS WITH A DOT •
TO FORM THIS PICTURE.

MAZE
FOLLOW THE ROCK PATH TO THE ROLL!

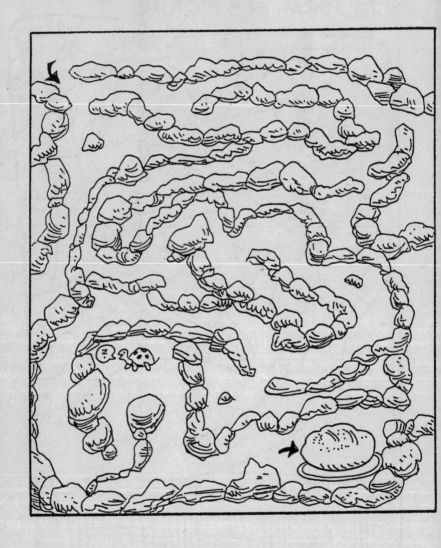

MYSTERY PIX

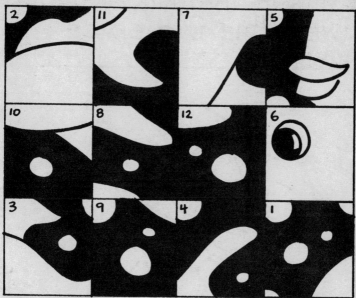

DRAW WHAT YOU SEE FROM THE NUMBERED BOXES
ABOVE INTO THE SAME NUMBERED BOXES BELOW.

1	2	3	4
5	6	7	8
9	10	11	12

FIND AND CIRCLE...

10 THINGS THAT ARE DIFFERENT BETWEEN THE TWO SPACE TRAVELERS.

HOMONYM TWISTER

HOMONYMS ARE WORDS THAT SOUND THE SAME BUT ARE SPELLED DIFFERENTLY AND HAVE DIFFERENT MEANINGS. CHOOSE THE CORRECT HOMONYM FOR EACH SENTENCE. THE FIRST ONE HAS BEEN DONE.

1- DOES SANTA RIDE IN A SLAY OR (SLEIGH)?

2- DO HORSES EAT HEY OR HAY?

3- DOES A ROUND BALL ROLL OR ROLE?

4- DOES FIVE MINUS THREE EQUAL TWO OR TOO?

5- DOES A POSTAL WORKER DELIVER MALE OR MAIL?

6- ARE THERE 7 DAYS IN A WEEK OR WEAK?

7- IS THE OPPOSITE OF YES KNOW OR NO?

MAZE LETTERS

TAKE THE LETTERS THROUGH THE MAZE TO FORM THE HIDDEN PHRASE.

IN SEARCH OF...

THE WORD **CHRISTMAS** APPEARS **5** TIMES IN THIS PUZZLE. FIND AND CIRCLE EACH ONE.

```
H R C H R T A C I I
I S H C I M S Y N C
C H R I S T M A S H
H C I H S R A S A R
R T S M C S R A R I
I C T H M M N M S S
S H M R L T S T Y T
T M A I A M Z S G M
M Y S S D F H I H A
A D C H S Y N R I S
S A M T S I R H C C
T M A M C M S C N Y
```

CITY MAZE

Travel through the city to find your way home.

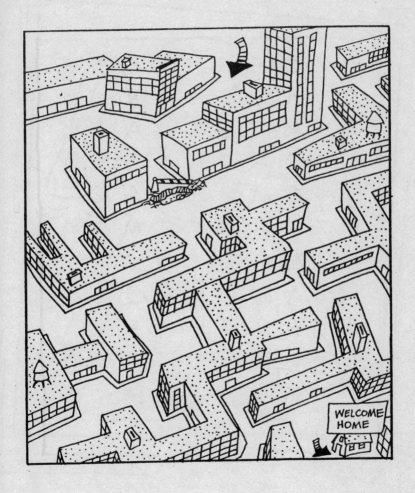

"BOO!" MAZE

DECODE

Use this chart to decode the secret message and find out something about Peter Rabbit!

A	B	C	D	E	F	G	H	
15	12	18	22	4	1	17	24	

I	J	K	L	M	N	O	P	Q	R
2	26	13	11	16	25	3	7	21	9

S	T	U	V	W	X	Y	Z
5	8	14	19	23	10	20	6

7 4 8 4 9   11 2 13 4 5   8 3

7 11 15 20   23 2 8 24   24 2 5

1 9 2 4 25 22 5 .

71

GO TO THE BARN MAZE!

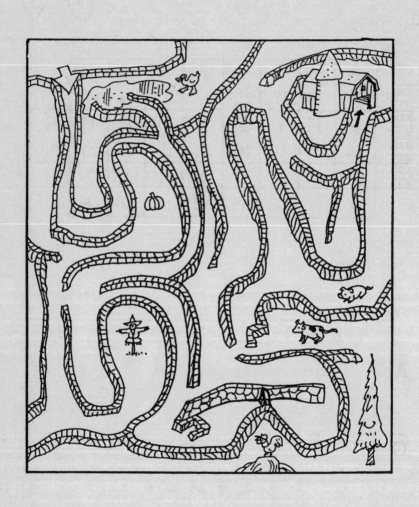

MORE

USE THIS CHART TO DECODE A HOLIDAY MESSAGE!

REAL LETTER	A	B	C	D	E	F	G	H	I	J	K	L	M
CODE LETTER	Z	X	L	V	B	N	M	A	S	D	F	G	H
REAL LETTER	N	O	P	Q	R	S	T	U	V	W	X	Y	Z
CODE LETTER	J	K	C	Q	W	E	R	T	Y	U	I	O	P

$\overline{A}\ \overline{Z}\ \overline{Y}\ \overline{B}\quad \overline{Z}\quad \overline{H}\ \overline{B}\ \overline{W}\ \overline{W}\ \overline{O}$

$\overline{G}\ \overline{S}\ \overline{R}\ \overline{R}\ \overline{G}\ \overline{B}$

$\overline{L}\ \overline{A}\ \overline{W}\ \overline{S}\ \overline{E}\ \overline{R}\ \overline{H}\ \overline{Z}\ \overline{E}$!

73

FLOWER TIME MAZE!

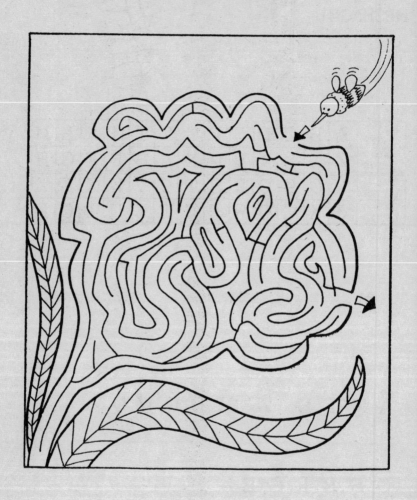

Mystery Word-Search Puzzle

HOME SWEET HOME

A-Apartment, Attic
B-Basement, Bath,
  Bedroom, Bell,
  Build
C-Cabinet, Carpet,
  Ceiling, Chandelier,
  Children, Clean,
  Clock, Closet, Color,
  Couch, Curtain
D-Decorate, Den,
  Desk, Dishwasher,
  Door
E-Entrance
F-Fashion, Family,
  Frame, Furnish,
  Furniture
G-Garage
H-Hang, Hassock,
  House

K-Kitchen, Knob
L-Lamp, Large,
  Laundry, Lawn,
  Level, Live
M-Mansion, Married,
  Mat, Mirror
O-Outlet, Oven
P-Paint, Panel, Piano,
  Picture, Private
R-Rug
S-Shade, Shower,
  Sink, Small, Stairs,
  Stereo, Stove, Style
T-Table, Toaster,
  Towel
V-Village
W-Window
Y-Yard

Write the uncircled letters in the space below. Then unscramble the letters to find out the Mystery Word.

scrambled letters clue: Metal rail

_____

mystery word:

_____

Find and circle the listed words. They go forward,
backward, up, down, or diagonally.

```
E G A L L I V D E C O R A T E
D I S H W A S H E R O O D O T
M C H A N D E L I E R U G A E
O E R U T I N R U F E S M S L
O I S I N K L A U N D R Y T T
R L N B A F A S H I O N N E U
D I E E E H S I N R U F R R O
E N D L L T Y B R Y L I M A F
B G Y L C A B I N E T B O N K
S T A I R S M P R I V A T E N
S A P D E S K P I C T U R E N
T B A S E M E N T P A I N T I
O L R H L E V E L O N A I P A
V E T O A N O I S N A M A I T
E L M W R S T E R E O V E N R
V A E E G E S U O H B A T H U
I W N R E C L O C K H C U O C
L N T T E S O L C L E N A P E
A R O N E H C T I K B U I L D
T O W I N D O W G A R A G E A
T L E C N A R T N E M A R F H
I O L D E I R R A M L L A M S
C C N E R D L I H C A R P E T
```

LOST PUPPIES

CAN YOU FIND THREE LOST PUPPIES IN
THIS CROWDED PARK? CIRCLE EACH ONE.

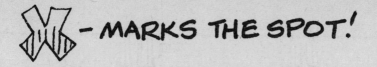 **– MARKS THE SPOT!**

COLOR IN BLACK ALL THE AREAS THAT
CONTAIN AN X TO FORM THIS SPOOKY
PICTURE!

A-MAZE-ING

Find your way through this maze to
where the toys are.

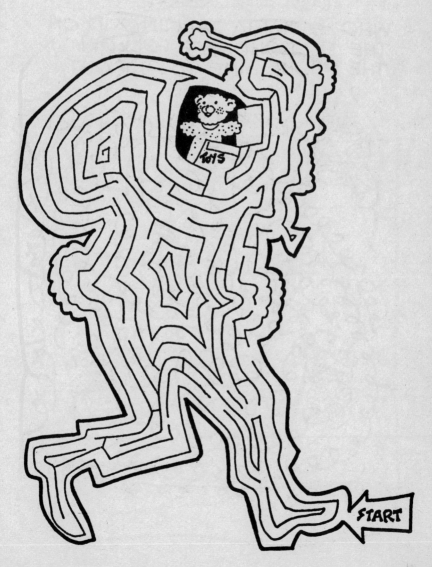

WHO IS MARIA TALKING TO ON THE TELEPHONE? FOLLOW THE PHONE LINE TO FIND OUT.

FLAVOR FUN

WHAT'S YOUR FAVORITE FLAVOR? PLACE THESE FLAVORS IN THEIR CORRECT SPACES.

4 LETTER WORD
LIME

5 LETTER WORDS
LEMON
PEACH

6 LETTER WORD
BANANA

7 LETTER WORD
VANILLA

9 LETTER WORDS
CHOCOLATE
RASPBERRY

10 LETTER WORD
STRAWBERRY

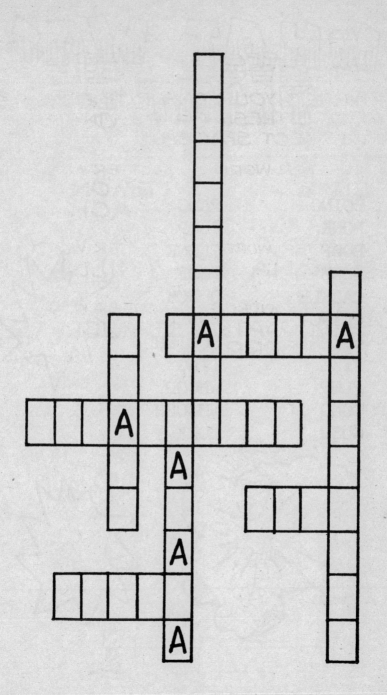

WHAT WAS THAT?

BOING	PANG
BONK	PLOP
BOOF	PLUNK
BUZZ	POOF
CACKLE	QUACK
CLANG	SNARL
CLINK	SQUISH
FIZZ	TING
FLOP	WHOOP
GONG	WHOOSH
GUSH	ZONK

Circle these **WACKY SOUNDS**.
They go up and down, across, backwards and diagonally.

```
F  B  G  T  J  P  L  O  P
Q  U  A  C  K  L  V  M  O
C  Z  H  S  I  U  Q  S  O
S  Z  N  Z  O  N  K  X  H
D  Z  W  G  C  K  P  G  W
Q  I  Y  N  N  N  N  U  H
G  F  O  O  B  I  P  S  O
N  N  B  G  T  L  O  H  O
A  N  A  J  M  C  L  B  S
L  L  F  P  O  O  F  O  H
C  A  C  K  L  E  I  R  U
T  C  P  K  L  R  A  N  S
```

CROSS OUTS

Cross out the letters **C, F, J, M**, and **V**.
Then, list the remaining letters in the blank spaces
to form a mystery word!

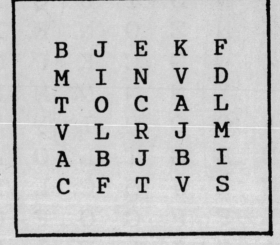

B J E K F
M I N V D
T O C A L
V L R J M
A B J B I
C F T V S

_ _   _ _ _ _   _ _

_ _ _   _ _ _ _ _ _ _ !

EGG MATCH

CAN YOU FIND AT LEAST
5 THINGS DIFFERENT
BETWEEN THESE 2 EGGS?

FIND and CIRCLE

CAN YOU FIND AND CIRCLE **10** THINGS
THAT DON'T BELONG IN THIS MEDIEVAL
CASTLE SCENE?

BALLET LINK-UP

WRITE THESE WORDS HAVING TO DO WITH THE BALLET IN THEIR CORRECT SPACES.

BALLERINA • DANCE • FEET • LEAP • MUSIC • PIROUETTE • TOES • TUTU •

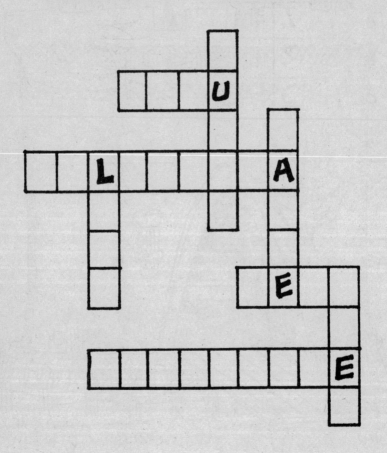

RIDDLE TIME

USE THE SPECIAL CHART TO
DECODE THE ANSWER TO THIS
RIDDLE.

WHAT DO YOU DO IF YOU HEAR A SNAKE RATTLE?

	1.	2.	3.	4.
A-	T	V	R	J
B-	E	R	I	A
C-	H	Q	P	D

___ ___ ___ ___   ___ ___
C-1 B-4 A-2 B-1   B-3 A-1

___ ___ ___ ___ ___ ___ ___ ___ !
A-3 B-1 C-3 B-4 B-3 B-2 B-1 C-4

A-MAZE-ING MOON

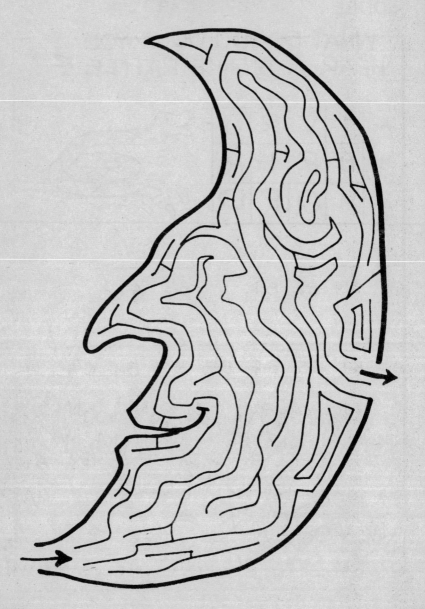

MAKE-A-WORD

Create your own list of words using the letters from:
MOVIE STAR

SEEK AND FIND

THE WORD **CARTOON** HAS
BEEN HIDDEN **10** TIMES IN
THIS PUZZLE. FIND AND
CIRCLE THEM.

```
C C C R N T A R C C
C A R T O O N N N N
R R R T N T N R C T
N T C T R T N C R R
O O C C O O C A N T
O O N N O O T R A C
T N T T N R N T R C
R R R C N R R O N T
A A N C A R T O O N
C C A R T O O N N N
N N N N O O T R A C
```

MAZE PHRASE

TAKE THE LETTERS THROUGH THE MAZE TO FORM THE HIDDEN PHRASE.

CAREFUL COUNT

HOW MANY CHRISTMAS BALLS DO YOU SEE?
COUNT CAREFULLY AS MANY OVERLAP.

TOTAL: _____

OPPOSITES

WRITE THE OPPOSITE OF EACH WORD AND PLACE THE CIRCLED LETTERS IN NUMBER ORDER TO COMPLETE THIS SENTENCE.

U P   ◯◯ _ _
           8 2

Y E L L   _ ◯◯ _ _ _ _ ◯
           10 7   6

F A L S E   ◯◯ _ ◯
          4 12   11

P U P P Y   ◯ _ ◯ _ _ ◯
        13   9   3

S H A L L O W   ◯ _ ◯ _
          1   5

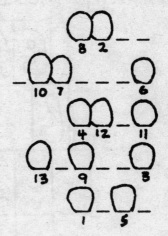

$\overline{1}\,\overline{2}\,\overline{3}$ ' $\overline{4}$ B $\overline{5}$ A F $\overline{6}$ A $\overline{7}\,\overline{8}$ OF

$\overline{9}\,\overline{10}\,\overline{11}$ D A $\overline{12}\,\overline{13}$!

WALL WORDS

COMPLETE THIS WALL
BY USING THE LETTERS
IN THE TOP WORD TO
COMPLETE THE OTHERS.
SOME LETTERS MAY BE
USED MORE THAN ONCE.

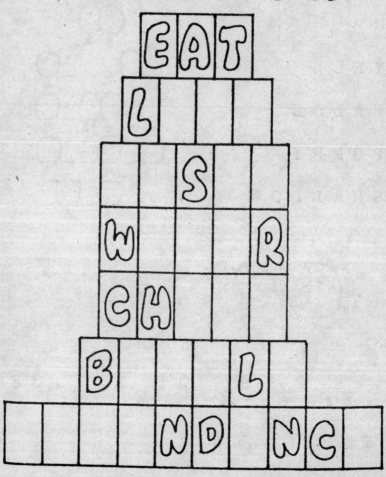

101

WHICH IS DIFFERENT?

THEY ALL LOOK THE SAME BUT
ONE IS DIFFERENT – FIND IT!

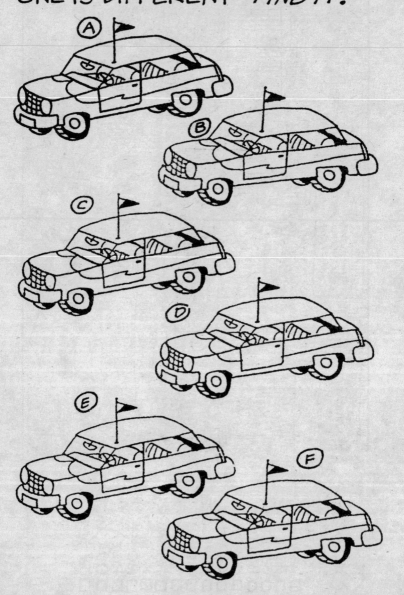

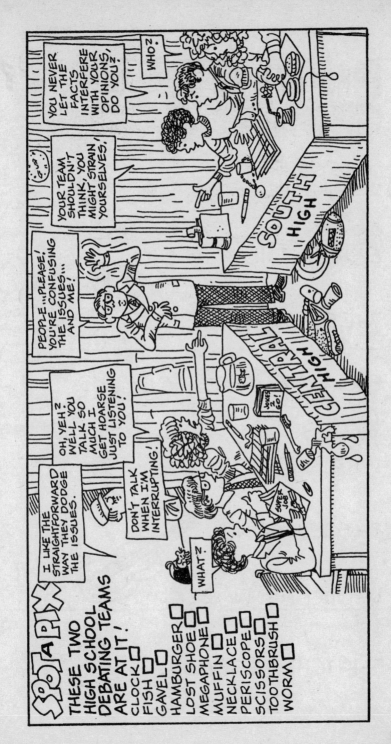

103

PICTURE CROSSWORD

ACROSS –
2– FAMILY PET

6–IT OPENS A LOCK

7–ESKIMO HOUSE

8–CARPENTER'S TOOL

DOWN –
1–RAIN PROTECTOR

3– SIX STRING

4–CIRCUS WORKER

5–KITCHEN UTENSIL

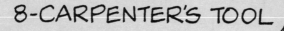

ALL SPORTS

WHAT'S YOUR FAVORITE SPORT?
FIND AND CIRCLE THIS LIST OF
SPORTS WORDS IN THIS PUZZLE.

- [ ] BASEBALL
- [ ] BASKETBALL
- [ ] BOWLING
- [ ] CATCH
- [ ] FIELD
- [ ] FOOTBALL
- [ ] GOLF
- [ ] HOCKEY
- [ ] JUMP
- [ ] LACROSSE
- [ ] RACKET
- [ ] SKATE
- [ ] SLIDE
- [ ] SOCCER
- [ ] SOFTBALL
- [ ] SWING
- [ ] TEAM
- [ ] TENNIS
- [ ] THROW

```
B S E G N I L W O B
L A R E C C O S H C
L A C R O S S E K Y
L L T N G L J U M P
A T H R O W T A E F
B E O C F I E L D O
T N C F T T L C I O
F N K D S A C R L T
O I E N B W C E S B
S S Y E T A K S F A
B A S K E T B A L L
G A V G N I W S O L
B R A C K E T N G S
```

UNSCRAMBLE THESE
WORDS HAVING TO DO WITH
WINTER CLOTHING. WRITE
THE CIRCLED LETTERS IN
THE SAME NUMBERED SPOTS
BELOW TO COMPLETE THE
SENTENCE.

WTEESAR

◯ ◯ _ _ _ _ ◯ ◯
3 7   11 5

RFACS

◯ _ _ _ ◯ _
12   1

BSOTO

_ _ ◯ ◯ _ _
  9 14

TNMESIT

◯ _ ◯ _ ◯ ◯ _
6   10   2 13

OTCA

_ ◯ ◯ _
  8 4

D _ _ _ S W _ _ _
  1 2 3   4 5 6
_ HEN Y _ U GO _ U _
7   8   9   10
IN TH _ _ _ _ W !
       11   12 13 14

GHOST WALL

Help this ghost fill in the wall by using only the
letters in the top word to complete the other words.
Some letters may be used more than once.

WHAT'S WRONG?

CAN YOU FIND AND CIRCLE **10** THINGS
THAT DON'T BELONG IN THIS SCENE?

FIND the WORDS

AGE	GROW
BIRTH	MAIL
CAKE	MATURE
CANDLES	OLDER
CHANGE	PARTY
DATE	PLAY
ENJOY	RECEIVE
GAMES	YEAR
GIFTS	YOUNG
	WISH

Circle these words about **BIRTHDAYS**.
They go up and down, across, backwards
and diagonally.

```
C  W  R  E  D  L  O  B  G
S  T  F  I  G  M  J  T  L
L  G  B  F  D  A  G  W  H
R  K  M  A  H  T  R  I  B
A  Q  T  L  G  U  S  S  P
E  E  T  I  R  R  S  H  S
Y  S  C  A  K  E  O  S  E
T  U  H  M  L  N  X  W  M
R  L  A  D  V  J  I  O  A
A  R  N  A  Y  O  U  N  G
P  A  G  U  E  Y  A  L  P
C  C  E  V  I  E  C  E  R
```

SANTA'S CROSSWORD

Help Santa complete this holiday crossword puzzle.

ACROSS

1. COLOR OF SANTA'S SUIT
5. THEY CELEBRATED THE FIRST THANKSGIVING
6. IT GOES "GOBBLE! GOBBLE!"

DOWN

2. SPRINGTIME HOLIDAY
3. 12TH MONTH OF THE YEAR
4. JINGLE _____

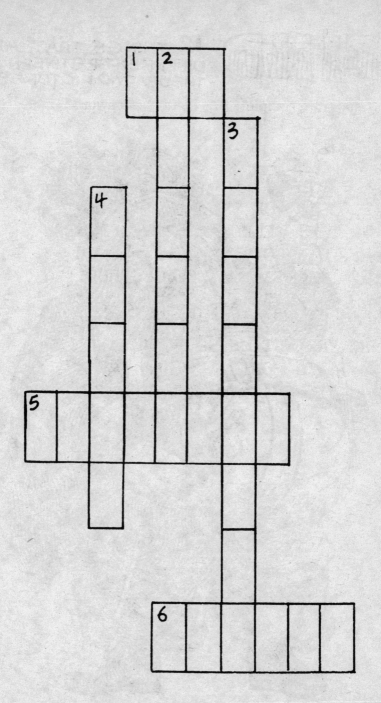

FIND

12 THINGS THAT ARE DIFFERENT BETWEEN THESE TWO PICTURES.

WORD FIND

BALL GAME	JUNE
BUDDY	MAN
DADDY	POPS
FAMILY	SHOW
GREAT GUY	SLIPPERS
HELP	SPECIAL DAY
HUSBAND	SUNDAY
LOVE	TIES

Circle these words about **FATHER'S DAY**.
They go up and down, across, backwards
and diagonally.

```
B  S  R  E  P  P     I  L  S
A  H  Y  G  C  S  P  O  P
L  O  D  L  D  O  Q  V  E
L  W  D  E  P  P  H  E  C
G  Y  A  D  N  U  S  G  I
A  S  D  F  S  H  O  R  A
M  M  H  B  E  E  E  R  L
E  F  A  M  I  L  Y  A  D
O  N  H  N  F  P  R  T  A
D  S  U  S  E  I  T  G  Y
E  A  S  J  S  E  C  U  D
T  J  T  B  U  D  D  Y  Q
```

MAZE

Help these elves deliver Santa's mail by correctly
traveling through this maze!

BATTER UP?

FIND AND CIRCLE **6** THINGS THAT
DON'T BELONG IN THIS SCENE.

Cross out the letters **B, D, G, L** and **P**.
List the remaining letters in the blank spaces to
form this Halloween phrase.

T	R	B	P	I
D	L	C	G	K
O	P	L	D	R
B	G	T	R	E
D	P	A	L	T

_ _ _ _ _   _ _   _ _ _ _ _ !

SCHOOL DAYS

PLACE THESE WORDS HAVING TO DO WITH SCHOOL IN THEIR CORRECT SPACES IN THE BLANK GRID.

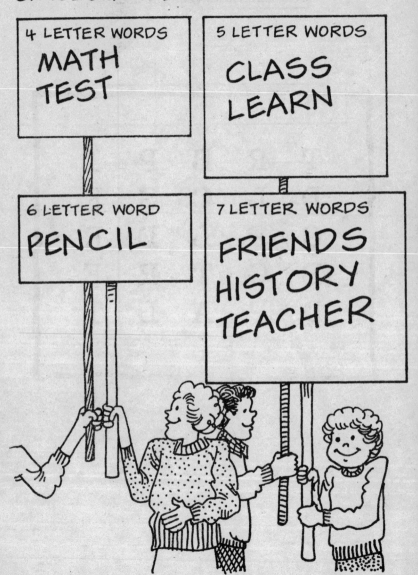

4 LETTER WORDS
MATH
TEST

5 LETTER WORDS
CLASS
LEARN

6 LETTER WORD
PENCIL

7 LETTER WORDS
FRIENDS
HISTORY
TEACHER

SCHOOL FIND

WHAT WORDS COME TO MIND WHEN YOU THINK OF SCHOOL? BELOW ARE A FEW THAT YOU CAN FIND AND CIRCLE IN THE DIAGRAM.

- BOOKS
- CLASS
- DESK
- GYM
- HISTORY
- HOMEWORK
- LEARN
- LESSON
- LUNCH
- MATH
- PAPER
- PENCIL
- TEACHER
- TEST
- TEXT

They go up and down, across, backwards and diagonally.

```
D T S K O O B L Y
C E T T R O C E V
O G S L X L R S Y
R Y E K U E S S R
E M T N H A T O O
P L C C L R H N T
A H A C Y N T L S
P E N C I L A E I
T K R O W E M O H
```

BULL'S-EYE

WHICH ARROW WILL HIT THE BULL'S-EYE?

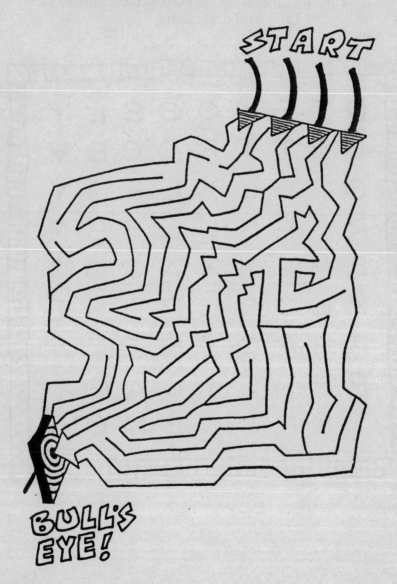

START

BULL'S EYE!

CROSS OUTS

Cross out all the letters that appear 4 times.
List the remaining letters in the spaces
below to form a question.

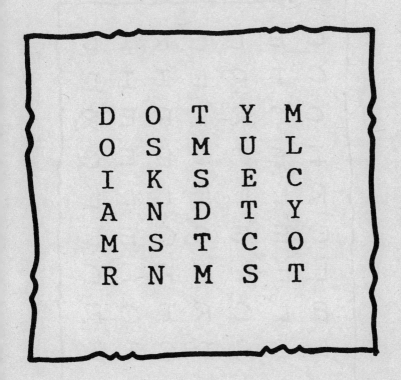

D O T Y M
O S M U L
I K S E C
A N D T Y
M S T C O
R N M S T

_ _ _ _ _ _ _ _ _ _

_ _ _ _ _ _ _ _ _ _ ?

CIRCLING CIRCLES

The word **CIRCLE** appears 8 times in this grid—find and circle each.

```
C E L C R I C
C I R L I I I
C C R R R E R
I E C C E E C
R L L L L L L
C E E C C E E
L E L C R I C
E L C R I C R
L C R I C I I
```

HIDDEN NUMBERS

HIDDEN IN THIS SCENE ARE THE
NUMBERS **1** THROUGH **10**.
FIND AND CIRCLE EACH.

DECODE

USE THIS CHART TO DECODE THE SPOOKY MESSAGE!

A	B	C	D	E	F	G	H	
26	25	24	23	22	21	20	19	

I	J	K	L	M	N	O	P	Q	R
18	17	16	15	14	13	12	11	10	9

S	T	U	V	W	X	Y	Z
8	7	6	5	4	3	2	1

$\overline{7}$ $\overline{4}$ $\overline{22}$ $\overline{15}$ $\overline{5}$ $\overline{22}$ $\overline{12}$ $\overline{24}$ $\overline{15}$ $\overline{12}$ $\overline{24}$ $\overline{16}$

$\overline{14}$ $\overline{18}$ $\overline{23}$ $\overline{13}$ $\overline{18}$ $\overline{20}$ $\overline{19}$ $\overline{7}$ $\overline{18}$ $\overline{8}$ $\overline{7}$ $\overline{19}$ $\overline{22}$

!

$\overline{4}$ $\overline{18}$ $\overline{7}$ $\overline{24}$ $\overline{19}$ $\overline{18}$ $\overline{13}$ $\overline{20}$ $\overline{19}$ $\overline{12}$ $\overline{6}$ $\overline{9}$

WALK DOWN

YOU'RE ON THE TOP FLOOR AND
THE ELEVATORS HAVE STOPPED
RUNNING. YOU NOW MUST
WALK DOWN.

STREET

SECRET JOKE

USE THE CHART TO DECODE THE ANSWER TO THIS JOKE.

WHAT DID ONE POTATO CHIP SAY TO THE OTHER ?

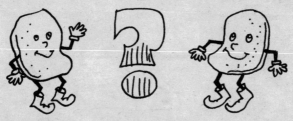

A	B	C	D	E	F	G	H	I	J	K	L	M
□	■	□□	■■	□■	■□	☆	★	☆☆	★★	☆★	★☆	△

N	O	P	Q	R	S	T	U	V	W	X	Y	Z
▲	△△	▲▲	▲△	▲△	□☆	■☆	☆△	★▲	□△	■▲	△☆	▲★

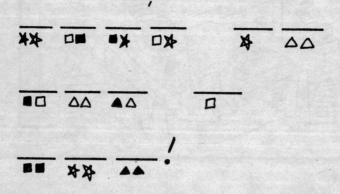

LET'S GO

FOR A

DIP!

DECODE-A-RIDDLE

WHY DID THE MAD SCIENTIST TELL THE ZOMBIE TO GET SOME REST ?

USE THIS SPECIAL CHART TO DECODE THE ANSWER.

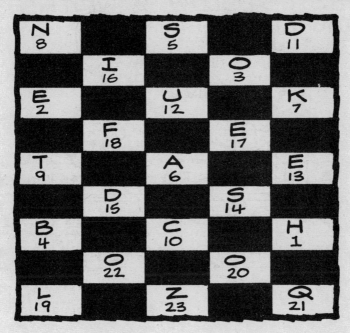

$\overline{4}$ $\overline{2}$ $\overline{10}$ $\overline{6}$ $\overline{12}$ $\overline{14}$ $\overline{13}$ $\overline{1}$ $\overline{13}$

$\overline{19}$ $\overline{20}$ $\overline{22}$ $\overline{7}$ $\overline{13}$ $\overline{11}$

$\overline{11}$ $\overline{2}$ $\overline{6}$ $\overline{15}$ $\overline{3}$ $\overline{8}$

$\overline{1}$ $\overline{16}$ $\overline{5}$ $\overline{18}$ $\overline{13}$ $\overline{17}$ $\overline{9}$ **!**

135

MISSING LETTERS

WHAT'S GOOD TO DRINK ON A COLD DAY? COMPLETE THE PUZZLE BELOW BY WRITING THE MISSING LETTERS.

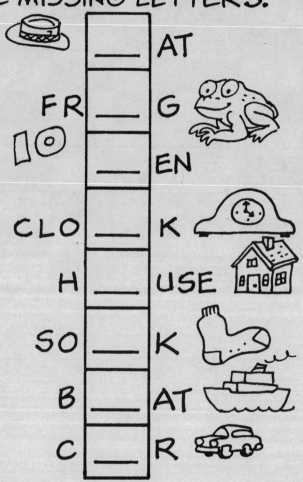

	___	AT
FR	___	G
	___	EN
CLO	___	K
H	___	USE
SO	___	K
B	___	AT
C	___	R

MISSING VOWELS

THESE WORDS ARE MISSING THEIR VOWELS **A·E·I·O·U**. WRITE THE CORRECT VOWELS IN THE RIGHT SPACES — THE CLUES WILL HELP YOU.

_ C T _ B _ R
(HALLOWEEN MONTH)

B _ _ C H
(SAND AND SURF)

L _ T T L _
(NOT BIG)

L _ N C H
(NOON TIME MEAL)

C L _ _ D S
(WHITE AND FLUFFY IN THE SKY)

F _ _ R T H
(.... OF JULY)

_ _ S Y
(NOT DIFFICULT)

MAKE-A-WORD

Create your own list of words using the letters from:
SLUMBER PARTY

HIDDEN WORD

Write the opposite of each word. The first letter of
each word, when read straight down in a line, will
spell the hidden word.

↓

SLOW	___ __ __ __
FAKE	___ __ __ __
OUT	___ __
DIFFICULT	___ __ __ __
SOUTH	___ __ __ __ __
UP	___ __ __ __
HAPPY	___ __ __

RIDDLE THIS:

WHAT DID THE MOTHER GHOST SAY TO HER BABY GHOST ?

USE THIS SPECIAL CHART TO DECODE THE ANSWER.

	A	B	C	D	E
1-	O	N	S	T	Y
2-	P	E	L	K	N
3-	U	T	O	R	I
4-	E	A	D	P	N

___ ___ ___ ___'
4C   1A   2E   3B

___ ___ ___ ___ ___
1C   4D   3C   1A   2D

___ ___ ___ ___ ___   ___ ___ ___
3A   1B   1D   3E   2C   1E   1A   3A

___ ___ ___
4B   3D   4A

___ ___ ___ ___ ___ ___ ___   ___ ___
1C   2A   3C   1A   2D   2B   4E   1D   3C

140

CROSSWORDS

COMPLETE THIS CROSSWORD
PUZZLE.

ACROSS
3. FROZEN WATER
5. _ _ _ _ _ _ HOG DAY
6. LARGE KITTEN

DOWN
1. THREE PLUS THREE =
2. A WINTER MONTH
4. PRESIDENT ABRAHAM
   _ _ _ _ _ _ _

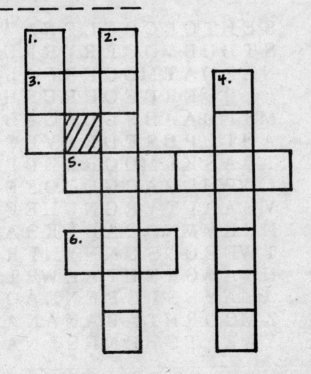

141

CIRCLE IT

Find and circle these **MORNING** words.
They go up and down, across, backwards,
and diagonally.

A—Alarm, Arise, Awake; **B**—Bacon, Bagel,
Banana, Bathroom, Bedroom, Brush; **C**—Cereal,
Clothes, Cold, Coffee, Comb; **D**—Danish, Donut,
Drive; **E**—Eggs, Exercise; **F**—Food; **G**—Groggy;
H—Hazy, Hungry, Hurry; **J**—Juice; **K**—Kitchen;
L—Late; **M**—Milk, Morning; **N**—Newspaper; **O**—
Oatmeal; **R**—Radio; **S**—Shave, Shower, Sunny,
Sunrise; **T**—Tired, Toast, Traffic; **V**—Vitamins;
W—Waffles, Wash, Weather; **Y**—Yawn

```
S E H T O L C S E L F F A W F
S T D U B M O C R R Y R R U H
N A E N A T M E C E R E A L J
I L R O E R P E O B R U S H U
M S I D A A B F L L E G A B I
A H T L P D S F D R I V E C C
T O A S K I M O O R D E B I E
I W W H L O A C G D O O F F S
V E A A I T Y R G N U H E F I
N R K V M N O C A B I K S A R
T W E E G G S U N N Y N I R N
H S A W G R E H T A E W R T U
A L A Y E S I C R E X E A O S
Z M O O R H T A B A N A N A M
Y A K I T C H E N H S I N A D
```

SPOT A PIX

SAY "CHEESE"!

- BAT ☐
- BROOM ☐
- CLOWN ☐
- DOORKNOB ☐
- FLOWER ☐
- ICE CREAM CONE ☐
- KITE ☐
- PAIL ☐
- PINWHEEL ☐
- TEDDY BEAR ☐
- UMBRELLA ☐
- VOLCANO ☐
- WAGON ☐
- YO-YO ☐

TAKE THE LETTERS THROUGH THE MAZE TO FORM THE HIDDEN PHRASE.

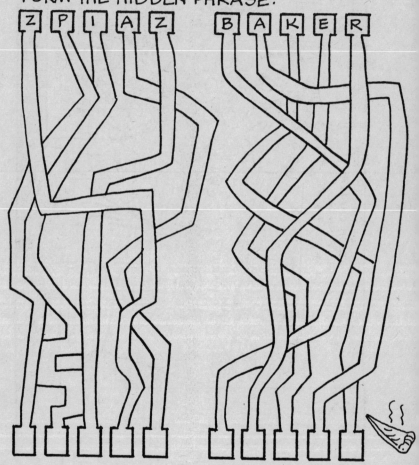

DIG OUT

HOW MANY SNOW SHOVELS
CAN YOU COUNT? COUNT
CAREFULLY, AS MANY OF
THEM OVERLAP.

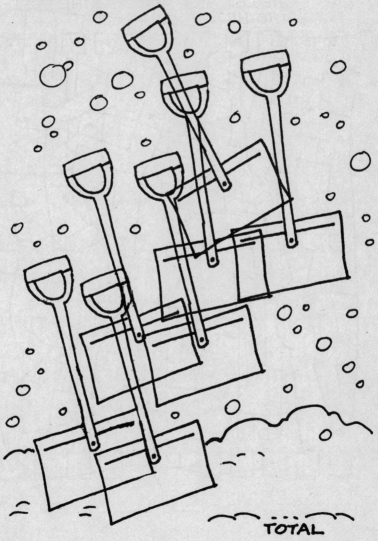

TOTAL

FILL IN

Fill in the areas that contain a dot to reveal this holiday message.

WHAT'S WRONG?

FIND **6** THINGS WRONG HERE

CARROT HUNT

HOW MANY CARROTS ARE HIDDEN IN
THIS PICTURE? CIRCLE EACH ONE.

TOTAL NUMBER OF CARROTS _____

ANIMAL NAMES

PLACE THE NAMES OF THESE ANIMALS IN THE PUZZLE BELOW.

CAMEL • CAT • COW • DOG • ELEPHANT • ROOSTER • SKUNK • SQUIRREL •

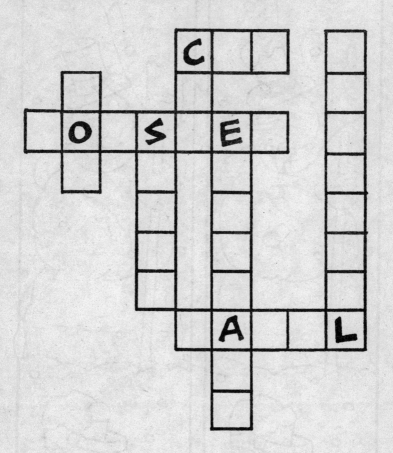

TWINS ?

FIND **6** THINGS THAT ARE
DIFFERENT BETWEEN THESE
TWO SNOWMEN AND CIRCLE THEM.

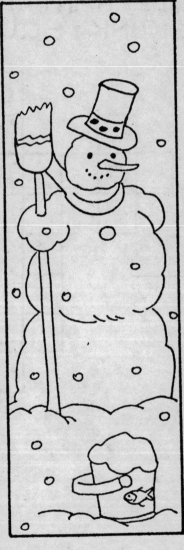

FROM A TO Z

TRAVEL THROUGH THIS
ALPHABET MAZE CORRECTLY
GOING FROM **A** TO **Z**.

151

ANSWERS TO PUZZLES

Page 4

Page 5

Page 6

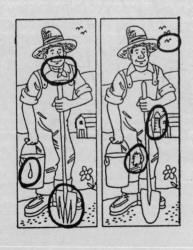

Page 7

	1.	2.	3.
1.	S	I	T
2.	I	C	E
3.	T	E	N

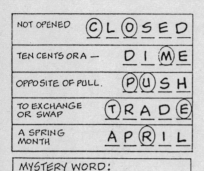

NOT OPENED	C L O S E D
TEN CENTS OR A —	D I M E
OPPOSITE OF PULL.	P U S H
TO EXCHANGE OR SWAP	T R A D E
A SPRING MONTH	A P R I L

MYSTERY WORD:

C O M P U T E R

Here are only some of the words
you can make from:
EASTER EGG

age	gate	stage
are	gear	stagger
ear	get	star
ease	reset	steer
east	sat	tag
eat	sear	tar
eggs	see	tear
erase	set	tease
gas	stag	tree

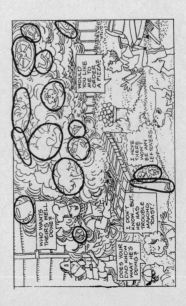

Page 12

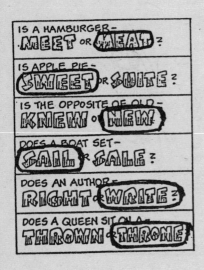

IS A HAMBURGER—
MEET OR MEAT?

IS APPLE PIE—
SWEET OR SWITE?

IS THE OPPOSITE OF OLD—
KNEW OR NEW?

DOES A BOAT SET—
SAIL OR SALE?

DOES AN AUTHOR—
RIGHT OR WRITE?

DOES A QUEEN SIT ON A—
THROWN OR THRONE

Page 13

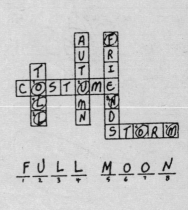

$\underline{F}_1 \underline{U}_2 \underline{L}_3 \underline{L}_4 \quad \underline{M}_5 \underline{O}_6 \underline{O}_7 \underline{N}_8$

Page 14

Page 15

2ND PRESIDENT

JOHN

AAMDS
ADAMS

4TH PRESIDENT

JAMES

DIMANSO
MADISON

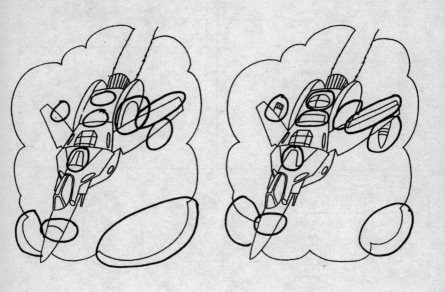

LNDA
LA(N)D

LGAD
(G)LAD

RAIPL
A(PRI)L

SUHOE
(H)OU(SE)

SYON
(N)OSY

OLDSI
(SO)LID

THIS HAPPENS EVERYTIME YOU STEP INTO THE SHOWER...

SCRAMBLED LETTERS:
NGPRIHENSO

UNSCRAMBLED ANSWER:
THE P H O N E R I N G S !!

Page 20

W H I S T L E
B3 D5 B1 D3 A4 C2 A2

L I K E
A5 D4 D1 C5

A
C3

B I R D !
C1 A3 B4 A1

Page 21

Pages 22-23

Page 24

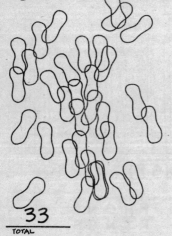

33
TOTAL

Page 25

Page 26

ARDGEN	11	GARDEN
UNF	2	FUN
OMM	6	MOM
HEPL	4	HELP
TEH	10	THE
IST'	1	IT'S
DDA	8	DAD
OT	3	TO
YROU	5	YOUR
NI	9	IN
ADN	7	AND

1. IT'S 2. FUN 3. TO
4. HELP 5. YOUR
6. MOM 7. AND 8. DAD
9. IN 10. THE
11. GARDEN.

Page 27

Pages 28-29

Pages 30-31

COLUMBUS DAY

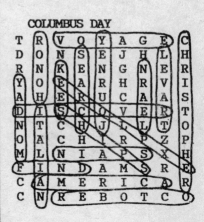

157

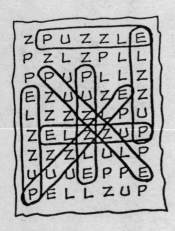

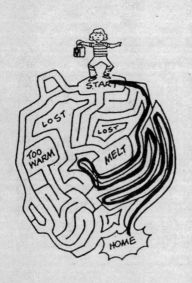

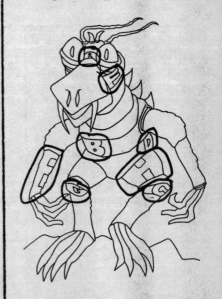

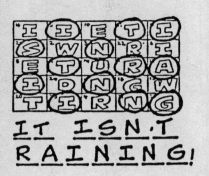

IT ISN'T
RAINING!

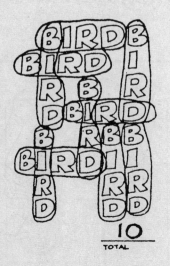

10
TOTAL

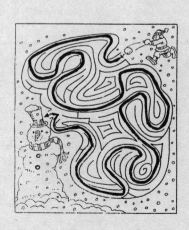

Page 40

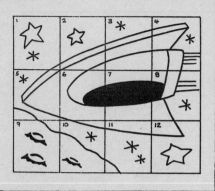

Page 41

Pages 42-43

Page 44

Page 45

GO THROUGH THIS MAZE, USING A DARK PENCIL, TO SEE WHAT'S HIDDEN HERE.

Page 46

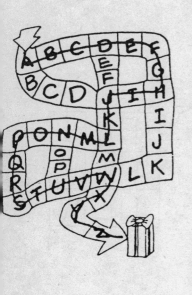

Page 47

Pages 48-49

```
C O W       P
  A         O
  S         P
  H         C
P I L O T   O     S
  N         R     I
  G     N O R T H
L E F T     
  O
M O N D A Y
```

Pages 50-51

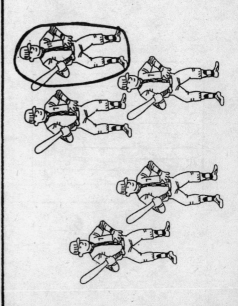

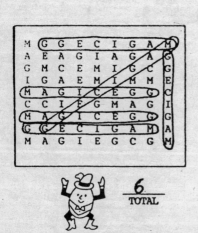

```
Ⓓ  L  E  ⓐ  T  ⓧ
S  L  Ⓡ  I  Ⓞ  G
ⓧ  Ⓛ  H  T  ⓧ  ⓧ  Ⓖ
ⓧ  Ⓗ  Ⓧ  T  H  ⓧ
E  T  Ⓥ  R  ⓧ  Ⓧ
ⓧ  Ⓧ  E  ⓧ  Ⓦ  E
```

L E T ' S

L I G H T   T H E

T R E E !

Here are only some of the words
you can make from:
VEGETABLE GARDEN

ad	glare	nerd
bean	grate	rage
beat	ladle	table
beg	lag	tag
dare	lard	tale
darn	leg	tar
den	nag	tear
get	near	teen
glade	neat	

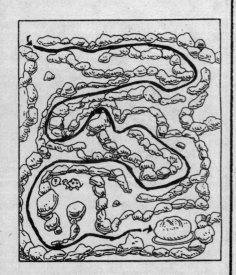

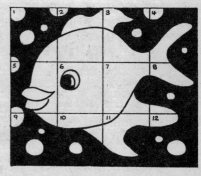

Pages 64-65

Page 66

1- DOES SANTA RIDE IN A
   SLAY OR (SLEIGH)?
2- DO HORSES EAT
   HEY OR (HAY)?
3- DOES A ROUND BALL
   (ROLL) OR ROLE?
4- DOES FIVE MINUS THREE
   EQUAL (TWO) OR TOO?
5- DOES A POSTAL WORKER
   DELIVER MALE OR (MAIL)?
6- ARE THERE 7 DAYS IN A
   (WEEK) OR WEAK?
7- IS THE OPPOSITE OF YES
   KNOW OR (NO)?

Page 67

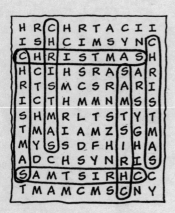

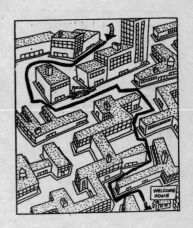

PETER LIKES TO
7 4 8 4 9   11 2 13 4 5   8 3

PLAY WITH HIS
7 11 15 20   23 2 8 24   24 2 5

FRIENDS.
1 9 2 4 25 22 5

Page 72

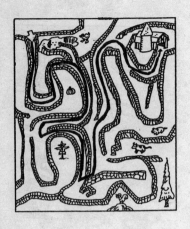

Page 73

H A V E A M E R R Y
A Z Y B Z H B W W O

L I T T L E
G S R R G B

C H R I S T M A S !
L A W S E R H Z E

Page 74

Page 75

Pages 76-77

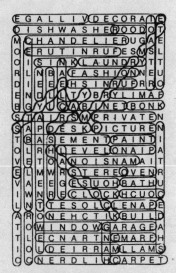

B A N N I S T E R

Pages 78-79

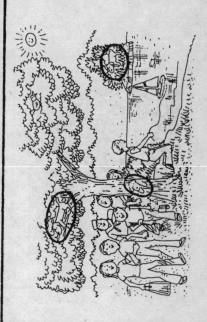

Page 80

Page 81

168

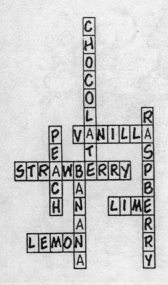

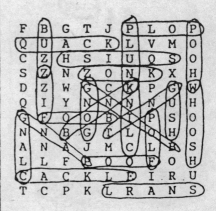

BE KIND TO
ALL RABBITS!

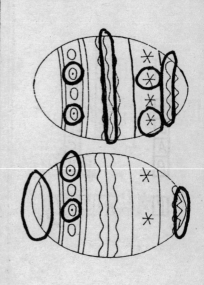

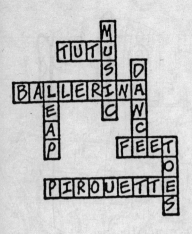

<u>H</u> <u>A</u> <u>V</u> <u>E</u>   <u>I</u> <u>T</u>
C-1. B-4 A-2 B-1   B-3 A-1

<u>R</u> <u>E</u> <u>P</u> <u>A</u> <u>I</u> <u>R</u> <u>E</u> <u>D</u>!
A-3 B-1 C-3 B-4 B-3 B-2 B-1 C-4

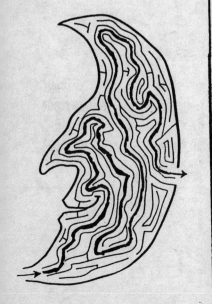

Here are only some of the words
you can make from:
MOVIE STAR

ear	rat	tame
east	rate	tar
eat	rave	tea
emit	roam	tear
mar	roe	tie
mare	rote	time
mat	sat	vase
more	seat	vet
move	smear	vie
oar	soar	vise
omit	stare	vista
or	stem	
over	stove	

171

Page 96

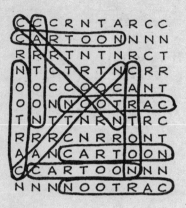

Page 97

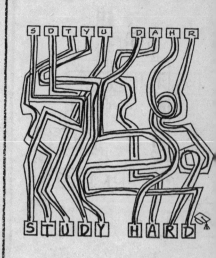

Page 98

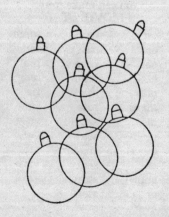

TOTAL: 8

Page 99

UP	DOWN
YELL	WHISPER
FALSE	TRUE
PUPPY	KITTEN
SHALLOW	DEEP

DON'T BE AFRAID OF THE DARK!

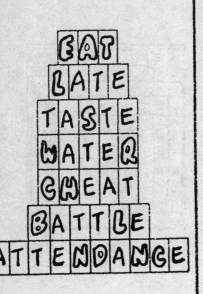

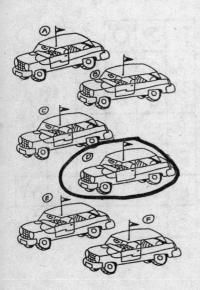

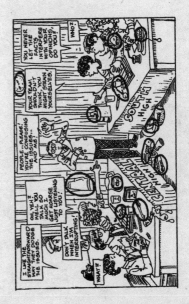

Pages 104-105

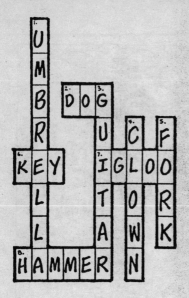

Pages 106-107

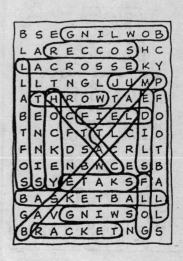

Page 108

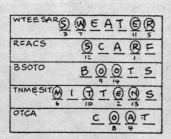

Page 109

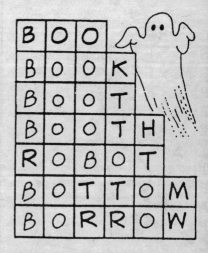

Pages 110-111

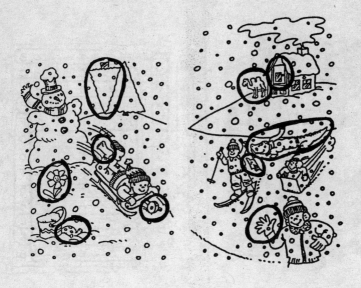

Pages 112-113

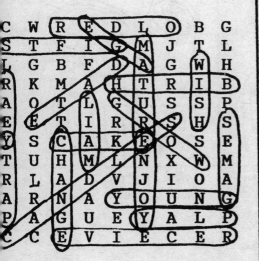

Pages 114-115

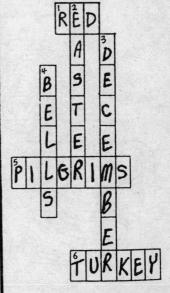

175

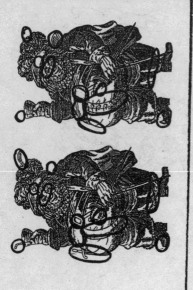

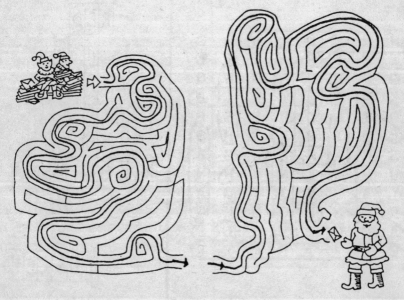

Page 122

Page 123

TRICK OR TREAT!

Pages 124-125

Pages 126-127

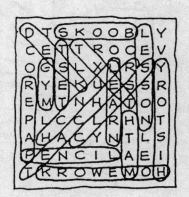

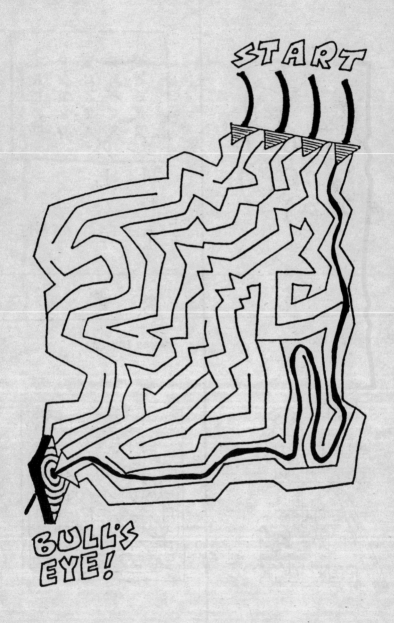

D O Y O U L I K E

C A N D Y - C O R N ?

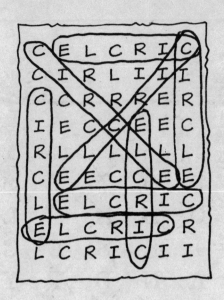

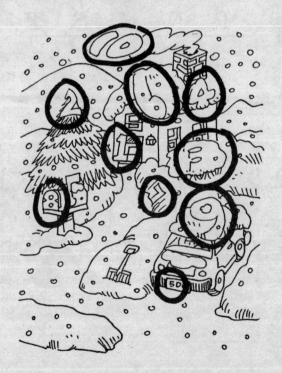

T W E L V E   O'C L O C K
7 4 22 15 5 22   12 24 15 12 24 16

M I D N I G H T   I S   T H E
14 18 23 13 18 20 19 7   18 8   7 19 22

W I T C H I N G   H O U R !
4 18 7 24 19 18 13 20   19 12 6 9

STREET

L E T ' S   G O
F O R   A
D I P !

B E C A U S E   H E
4 2 10 6 12 14 13   1 13

L O O K E D
19 20 22 7 13 11

D E A D   O N
11 2 6 15   3 8

H I S   F E E T !
1 16 5   18 13 17 9

H AT

FR O G

TEN

CLO C K

H O USE

SO C K

B O AT

C A R

Page 137

O C T O B E R (HALLOWEEN MONTH)
B E A C H (SAND AND SURF)
L I T T L E (NOT BIG)
L U N C H (NOON TIME MEAL)
C L O U D S (WHITE AND FLUFFY IN THE SKY)
F O U R T H (.... OF JULY)
E A S Y (NOT DIFFICULT)

Here are only some of the words
you can make from:
SLUMBER PARTY

bar	rare	slap
blur	rat	slump
brat	ray	slurp
burp	real	smear
lap	ream	sub
pal	rub	tab
part	rule	tar
rap	rust	team

	↓
SLOW	F AST
FAKE	R EAL
OUT	I N
DIFFICULT	E ASY
SOUTH	N ORTH
UP	D OWN
HAPPY	S AD

$$\underset{\text{4C}}{D}\ \underset{\text{1A}}{O}\ \underset{\text{2E}}{N}\ \underset{\text{3B}}{'T}$$

$$\underset{\text{1C}}{S}\ \underset{\text{4D}}{P}\ \underset{\text{3C}}{O}\ \underset{\text{1A}}{O}\ \underset{\text{2D}}{K}$$

$$\underset{\text{3A}}{U}\ \underset{\text{1B}}{N}\ \underset{\text{1D}}{T}\ \underset{\text{3E}}{I}\ \underset{\text{2C}}{L}\ \ \underset{\text{1E}}{Y}\ \underset{\text{1A}}{O}\ \underset{\text{3A}}{U}$$

$$\underset{\text{4B}}{A}\ \underset{\text{3D}}{R}\ \underset{\text{4A}}{E}$$

$$\underset{\text{1C}}{S}\ \underset{\text{2A}}{P}\ \underset{\text{3C}}{O}\ \underset{\text{1A}}{O}\ \underset{\text{2D}}{K}\ \underset{\text{2B}}{E}\ \underset{\text{4E}}{N}\ \ \underset{\text{1D}}{T}\ \underset{\text{3C}}{O}.$$

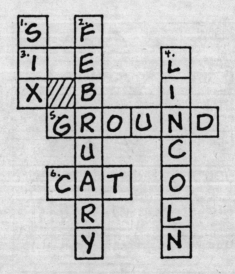

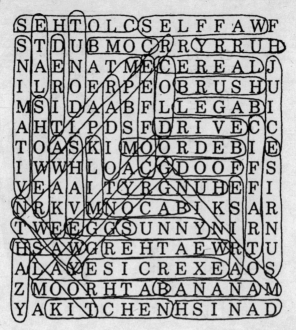

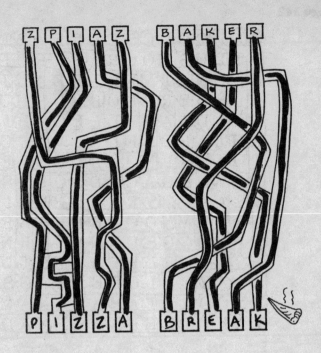

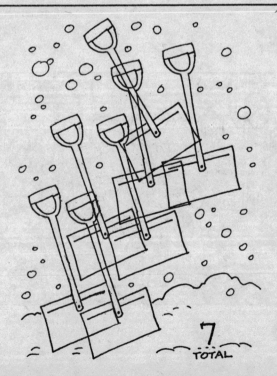

7
TOTAL

Page 148

TOTAL NUMBER OF CARROTS __6__

Page 149

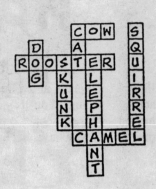

Page 150

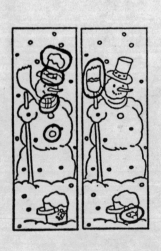

Page 151

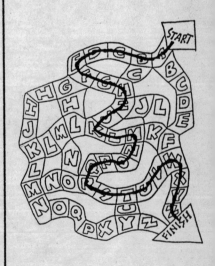

How to get *even MORE*

Pick up a pencil and plunge right in to the most awesome activities around. You'll find word searches, crosswords, mazes, hidden pictures, secret codes, mystery pictures to draw and **more**. Once you have one book, you'll want to collect them all!

Each book is
ONLY $2.50
plus $1.00 for
postage and handling.

— —

Send check or money order and coupon to:
KIDSBOOKS, INC.
3535 W. Peterson Ave.
Chicago, IL 60659

Enclosed is $_____ for _____ book(s) which includes postage and handling charges. (No COD's)

Check quantity for each:

_____#1	_____#4	_____#7	_____#10	_____#13	_____#16
_____#2	_____#5	_____#8	_____#11	_____#14	_____#17
_____#3	_____#6	_____#9	_____#12	_____#15	_____#18

Name_____

Address_____

City_____State_____Zip_____

Offer good for U.S. residents only.
Please allow 4-6 weeks for delivery.
Residents of Illinois please add the appropriate state and local sales tax.